life
beyond
earth & the
mind of
man

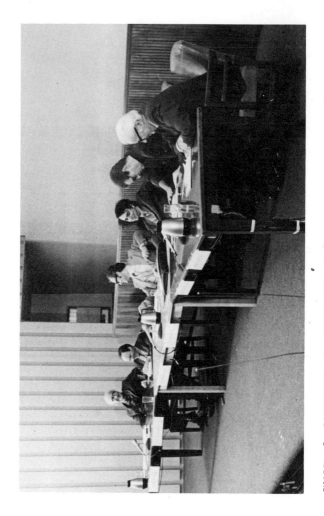

WALD • MORRISON • BERENDZEN • SAGAN • STENDAHL • MONTAGU

NASA SP–328

life beyond earth & the mind of man

EDITED BY RICHARD BERENDZEN

A symposium held at Boston University
on November 20, 1972

1973

NATIONAL AERONAUTICS AND SPACE ADMINISTRATION

Scientific and Technical Information Office • Washington, D.C.

For sale by the Superintendent of Documents, U.S. Government Printing Office
Washington, D.C. 20402 - Price $2
Stock Number 033-000-00518-1
Catalog Number NAS 1.21:328

Library of Congress Catalog No. 73-600150

Foreword

In considering the possible existence of extraterrestrial life, we have become accustomed to thinking of it chiefly in the context of our solar system. Yet in recent years information has accumulated that suggests, by some estimates of probability, that forms of life could be broadly distributed throughout the galaxy. It is within the realms of possibility, in fact, likely that technically advanced civilizations may exist on the planets of distant stars. Communications with such far-off islands of intelligence may someday be begun, with effects on man's home planet that can now be only imperfectly imagined.

A symposium to explore implications of this fascinating subject—the social, philosophic, and humanistic impact—was held in Boston last fall. Jointly sponsored by Boston University and NASA, the meeting brought out diverse viewpoints from a panel made up of two astronomers, a biologist, a physicist, an anthropologist, and a theologian, all of them men of distinction in their fields.

The text that follows is a slight abridgment of the transcript of this symposium. Many of the provocative and in some degree conflicting ideas expressed are worthy of consideration by thoughtful persons everywhere.

JAMES C. FLETCHER, *Administrator*
National Aeronautics and Space Administration

Contents

Berendzen

Welcome to the symposium on "Life Beyond Earth and the Mind of Man." Our topic will be the search for life in the universe and the ramifications of its possible discovery. Although there have been a handful of scientific meetings on this topic, to the best of my knowledge this is the first time there has ever been a meeting where a distinguished panel from diverse fields will discuss the topic in an open forum.

A generation ago almost all scientists would have argued, often *ex cathedra,* that there probably is no other life in the universe besides what we know here on Earth. But as Martin Rees, the cosmologist, has succinctly put it, "absence of evidence is not evidence of absence." Beyond that, in the last decade or so the evidence, albeit circumstantial, has become large indeed, so large, in fact, that today many scientists, probably the majority, are convinced that extraterrestrial life surely must exist and possibly in enormous abundance. The question now is no longer so much one of *if* as of *where,* and with regard to the search, it has also become *when,* for ultimate contact seems to many serious thinkers to be virtually inevitable. A short passage from the recent report of the Astronomy Survey Committee of the august National Academy of Sciences of the United States, the Nation's most distinguished scientific body, gives an example of the modern scientific attitude:

> Each passing year has seen our estimates of the probability of life in space increase, along with our capabilities for detecting it. More and more scientists feel that contact with other civilizations is no longer something beyond our dreams but a natural event in the history of mankind that will perhaps occur within the lifetime of many of us. The promise is now too great, either to turn away from it or to wait much longer before devoting major resources to a search for other intelligent beings. . . . In the long run this may be one of science's most important and most profound contributions to mankind and to our civilization.

I believe it fair to say, therefore, that this momentous topic deserves careful, thorough discussion, and that is what I hope we shall give it today.

2

AND THE MIND OF MAN

Let me introduce the panel. On the far side of the stage is Ashley Montagu, a renowed anthropologist and social biologist. For many years he was chairman of the Department of Anthropology at Rutgers. He is the author of scores of books and research papers on a variety of topics in the social sciences, including the social and cultural development of mankind.

Next to him is Krister Stendahl, an outstanding churchman and theologian, who is the Dean of the Harvard School of Divinity. Dr. Stendahl is widely considered to be one of the Nation's most scholarly theologians.

Next to me is Carl Sagan, an astronomer and exobiologist at Cornell University, and one of the five or six leading researchers on this question of extraterrestrial life. He is the coauthor with the Soviet astronomer I. S. Shklovskii of the book *Intelligent Life in the Universe.*

On my other side is Philip Morrison, a professor of physics at MIT. Thirteen years ago he coauthored what was perhaps the first scientifically valid and reasoned paper ever published on possible modes of communication with extraterrestrial life. Dr. Morrison is considered in scholarly circles as one of the most broadly knowledgeable scientists in the Nation.

And next to him is George Wald, a professor of biology at Harvard. In 1967 he received the Nobel Prize. Dr. Wald has published extensively in all branches of biology, including the biological and chemical evolution of terrestrial life.

I should stress, by the way, that the panelists were not chosen for homogeneity of view. Although it is obviously impossible to know what any of the panelists would say until the meeting has been held, insofar as I could guess their positions, I tried to arrange for diverse and divergent views.

The format will be as follows: Each of the other panelists will present a short statement on the topic as perceived from his particular field of expertise. After these introductory remarks, we shall have a free-flowing panel discussion, without a tight format, and then we will have questions and answers.

Sagan

Thomas Carlyle, a somewhat crusty old fellow, upon thinking about the stars, said: "A sad spectacle. If they be inhabited, what a scope for misery and folly. If they be not inhabited, what a waste of space." I suspect that in one way or another we will be returning to those two alternatives in this discussion. Is it possible that in a universe teeming with stars and planets there is not a multitude of other inhabited worlds? And if there is a multitude of inhabited worlds, then what is the nature of their inhabitants and what are the possible aspects of our contact with them?

I should stress that in the absence of any direct knowledge about the existence of extraterrestrial life or extraterrestrial intelligence at the present time, every remark, even ones by the prestigious National Academy of Sciences, has to be speculative. I will make such speculations, and I am sure others will also. But it is important to stress that people are making estimates by the seat of their pants, not on the basis of a careful study of large numbers of extraterrestrial life forms, which would be quite a different story.

There was, a little more than a year ago, in the Armenian Soviet Socialist Republic—in fact, at the foot of Mount Ararat on which Noah's ark was said to have been beached—a symposium sponsored jointly by the U.S. National Academy of Sciences and the Soviet Academy of Sciences on the question of contact with extraterrestrial intelligence. This was a 6-day meeting, which involved forty or fifty people, mostly from the United States and the U.S.S.R., but also from a few other nations.* In addition to physicists and astronomers, it involved biologists, chemists, anthropologists, archeologists, historians, and people concerned with coding messages and decoding them. It was a turning point, I think, in the study of the subject, not because some striking new opinions or results were expressed, but because it signified the increasing respectability of the subject. It is now OK to talk about life elsewhere or intelligent life elsewhere,

* *Communication with Extraterrestrial Intelligence* (publication in progress). MIT Press. Massachusetts Institute of Technology, Cambridge, Mass.

AND THE MIND OF MAN

whereas a decade or two ago it was not OK: It was considered too speculative to be worth any investment in time.

If we ask what is the likelihood that there are civilizations on planets of other stars—How many such societies might we expect there to be within our galaxy?—the answers depend upon a large number of factors, each of which is uncertain. Without giving any estimate of the numerical values, let me just state the kinds of things it depends on: how fast stars are made (the more there are, the more possible locales there are); how often stars have planets; how many planets in a given solar system might be suitable for life; the likelihood of the origin of life; the probability that once you have life going, you develop a form which we can call or they themselves can call "intelligent"; the likelihood that once you have an intelligent form it will develop a technical civilization (because they can be mighty smart, but if they do not have a technical civilization we're not likely to get in touch with them); and finally, the lifetime of the technical civilization. If all the preceding factors go swimmingly well but civilizations destroy themselves as soon as they develop radio telescopes, there will not be many organisms for us to talk to.

We debated these factors at the Byurakan Observatory for about half the meeting. There was not a unanimity of view as to how likely each of these things were. But what was clear was that the chances of there being extraterrestrial intelligence with which we could communicate were sufficiently high as to justify a search. And the critical point about the search is that human technology has now reached the point where we could detect ourselves at an enormous distance away. This can be put perhaps most dramatically by asking the following question: Suppose we took the world's largest steerable radio telescope—Cornell's dish at Arecibo, P.R.—in the form it will be in within another 2 or 3 years when it has been resurfaced and has a new transmitter, and imagine it in communication with an identical copy of itself. We move those two radio telescopes farther and farther away from each other. How far apart are they when they cannot make each other out anymore? The answer is that two such telescopes could talk to each other from anywhere within the galaxy; our present technology is able to detect ourselves anywhere in this galaxy of 250 billion stars.

AND THE MIND OF MAN

THE WORLD'S LARGEST STEERABLE RADIO TELESCOPE AT ARECIBO, PUERTO RICO.

It is, therefore, an extraordinary fact that we so far have listened to possible signals being sent our way from only a mere handful of stars. The first such effort was made more than 10 years ago in Project Ozma, organized by Frank Drake at the National Radio Astronomy Observatory. He looked for a couple of weeks at two stars at one frequency. The results were negative. In the meeting in Armenia a group from Gorki University, under V. S. Troitskii, announced that they had been making similar studies, looking at a dozen stars at two frequencies for slightly longer periods of time. No one was broadcasting from there. And Dr. Verschuur at the National Radio Astronomy Observatory has given me permission to make known at this meeting that he has performed recently a similar search at 21-centimeter wavelength with the 140- and 300-foot telescopes at Green Bank, West Virginia. He has looked at another handful of stars, and they were not sending anything either. His stars, just so you can get the flavor of the names of what is being listened to, are Barnard's Star, Wolf 359, Luyten 726–8, Lalande 21185, Ross 154, Ross 248, Epsilon Eridan, 61 Cygni, Tau Ceti, and 70 Ophiuchi. There was nobody around on those places a few years ago sending anything our way at 21 centimeters with the bandpass and time constant that Verschuur used.

The most optimistic estimates, in the view of many, about the number of civilizations that might be in the galaxy is on the order of a million, which means that only one in roughly 200 000 stars has such a civilization. Therefore, any search requires not a brief look but some substantial, long-term commitment of radio-telescope time.

I have been talking about listening. A question that is often asked or assumed is that we are sending. To the best of my knowledge there has never been a conscious attempt to send a radio message to a civilization on another star; however, there are a number of unconscious attempts. Some of the high-frequency end of the radio-broadcast band trickles out, and has been doing so since perhaps the 1920's and 1930's. So you can imagine a wavefront surrounding the Earth, traveling at the velocity of light, and carrying on it Duffy's Tavern, the 1928 election returns, and Enrico Caruso arias. It is faint, but it is out there. And you can imagine civilizations some thirty, forty, fifty light-years out, saying. "Ah, so *that's* what they were doing on

Earth fifty years ago!" There are a few other indications of intelligent life on Earth visible over interstellar distances. There is the radio that I mentioned; there is a lot of the content of domestic television; there are the radar defense networks of the United States and the Soviet Union; and there is some radar astronomy. That is a very interesting mix of signs of intelligent life on Earth, if you think about it. It is an extremely sobering thought, but that is the *only* sign of intelligent life on Earth that would be detectable over interstellar distances, which may explain how it is that nobody has been here.

I will close by saying that there has been one other attempt to send a message from the Earth to "out there." The NASA spacecraft Pioneer 10 is now halfway to Jupiter, in the asteroid belt and not having any trouble there. Once it passes Jupiter, in December of 1973, it will be the first manmade object to leave the solar system. That being the case, we thought it might be a good idea to put a little greeting card on it in case anyone picked it up some time later. So there is an aluminum plaque, which we succeeded in convincing NASA to bolt on to the spacecraft, and it is written very clearly

12

AND THE MIND OF MAN

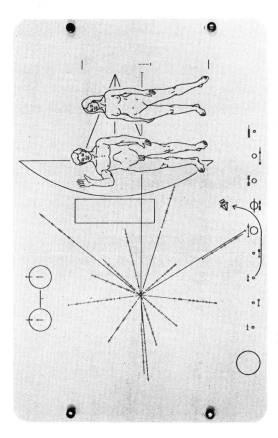

DESIGN ON PIONEER 10 PLAQUE USES BINARY NOTATION TO IDENTIFY 14 PULSARS IN RELATIONSHIP TO THE SUN, AND GIVES THEIR FREQUENCIES AT LAUNCH. THE DIAGRAM AT BOTTOM CHARACTERIZES SOLAR SYSTEM AND SPACECRAFT TRAJECTORY.

13

—not in English or Esperanto, because nobody out there speaks those languages—but in Scientific, which anybody who can intercept the spacecraft will surely speak. It says which star of the 250 billion in our galaxy sent this greeting card, and in which year in the 10-billion-year history of our galaxy it was sent. And then there are two quite mysterious objects on the plaque which they will never figure out. These objects are intended to indicate who sent the probe. So, while I think the chances of this message ever being intercepted are negligible, the sending of it has a symbolic significance in being the first conscious attempt by mankind to make contact with our brethren out there.

Wald

I think there is no question but that we live in an inhabited universe that has life all over it. I am interested in Carl Sagan's saying there are 250 billion stars like our Sun in our galaxy. I have been using the number "100 billion," but this is an inflationary period. I rather like Eddington's old paradigm for the situation: 10^{11} stars make a galaxy, 10^{11} galaxies make a universe. Those are good numbers still.

As for our own galaxy, it is estimated that perhaps 1 to 5 percent of the stars in it could provide on one or more of their planets an abode for life. That would mean 1 billion such places just in our own galaxy that might contain life. And as for what life would mean in those places, I think it would mean something very like the life we know. Not the same creatures. We did not have the same creatures on Earth during its past as live here now. But life anywhere in the universe, I have been convinced for years, must be made of the same elements that principally constitute it here—carbon, hydrogen, nitrogen, and oxygen. Those four elements constitute about 99 percent of living material on the Earth, and I think are likely to come out that way wherever life exists, because I believe it to be literally true that no other elements in the Periodic System have the properties that will do that job. So I tell my students: learn your biochemistry here and you will be able to pass examinations on Arcturus.

That brings us to a central problem: In that inhabited universe, where is our home as men? It seems to me that there is every probability, no matter what advances in technology are ever made, that our home in the universe is the solar system. I believe that we living things on the Earth constitute the only life in the solar system. The chance of breaking out of the solar system and establishing physical contact—or the chance of any creature in outer space establishing physical contact with us, coming to us from some other solar system—seems to me so remote as to be almost nil. In order to do that, one would have to travel at the speed of light and it is rather hard to travel at the speed of light and not be light. So I rather doubt that physical contact is possible.

16

AND THE MIND OF MAN

But we now are discussing another kind of contact, and that is communication. May I say, so that we can have a somewhat warmer and livelier conversation as this meeting goes on, that I can conceive of no nightmare as terrifying as establishing such communication with a so-called superior (or if you wish, advanced) technology in outer space. You see, I see no escape from the thought that more advanced technologies exist, very likely in a number of places within our own galaxy. That thought in itself is a little terrifying to me, I must say, because of my view of and identification with the human enterprise.

You see, when I ask myself as a lifelong scientist, "What's science about?" the answer is not to increase the catalog of facts, it is to achieve understanding. It means a great deal that one of the greatest human enterprises is our understanding. It is something that men have sweated out, to the greater dignity and worth of man. The thought that we might attach, as by an umbilical cord, to some more advanced civilization, with its more advanced science and technology, in outer space does not thrill me, but just the opposite. You see, I think it might thrill and fill with elation the people who did it; but that is true of almost any enterprise one could name, however horrifying, however destructive to the rest of mankind. You cannot think of anything so horrifying that some person would not have a feeling of personal accomplishment and elation at carrying it out; and I would say that the rest of us had better restrain him.

If one started some continuous transmission, it would be with creatures way ahead of where we are. How far ahead? A hundred years, a thousand, ten thousand, a million, why possibly even a billion! Unimaginably further ahead! Frank Drake, speaking about Project Ozma at the National Radio Astronomy Observatory, said the following, according to the *New York Times*. (Sometimes I turn into a kind of tape recorder, not always through admiration, and so I can quote the words as reported in the *Times*.) He said: "We'll have a lot of questions to ask those fellows. We'll ask them the cure for cancer and how to perform a controlled thermonuclear reaction." Well, you see, one of these days perhaps we will have a cure for cancer, and I will be proud of that, if I am still here. And I hope that before too long we will have worked out how to perform a controlled thermonuclear reaction, and I would be proud of that, too. But just to get such information passively from outer space through that transmission is altogether different. One could fold the whole human enterprise—the arts, literature, science, the dignity, the worth, the meaning of man—and we would just be attached as by an umbilical cord to that "thing out there."

One further thing I should like to raise as a question. Some years ago I heard the silly question asked: "Why is our world 4½ billion years old?" And the silly answer: "Because it took that long to find that out." That is a profound thought and it raises another thought that is meaningful in our time: When you have got to the point at which you find that out, have you got much longer to go? That is our problem. A lot of us do not quite see how to get beyond the next thirty years. Do you get much farther? *Are* there advanced civilizations in outer space? Not that they have not existed, and I rather think they do exist, but how much farther do they get? Do they all produce hydrogen bombs and engage in cold wars and stockpile enough stuff to wipe out all life on the surfaces of those planets? Can we keep the show on the road much longer?

Montagu

As Samuel Butler once remarked that life is the art of drawing sufficient conclusions from insufficient premises, the state of our present knowledge concerning life beyond Earth can perhaps, I think with some generosity, be described as the art of drawing insufficient premises from insufficient conclusions.

Let us begin, then, with a sufficient premise. When we speak of life beyond Earth, what we generally mean is, of course, intelligent life, something resembling our noble selves. It is highly probable that there are such intelligent forms of life in other galaxies in the universe, and it is even more probable that many of these forms are vastly more intelligent than we. This, of course, may be the principal reason why they have avoided establishing any form of communication with us, because if they have observed us, they no doubt regard us as we regard rabies or cancer or cholera—in short, as a highly infectious disease that is best quarantined from the rest of the universe.

Man as a species has been on this Earth for about 6 million years as that prematurely most officiously, arrogantly named species—homo sapiens, the wise guy. The proper appellation at the present time is "homo sap." Not that the wisdom is not there as a potentiality; it is. But the present state of his development suggests that he is no more than in a state of confusion. This 6 million years is for man as a food-gathering, hunting member of the species. The form in which we know him at the present time, as a dehumanized urban development, is only about 10 000 years old, whereas other forms of highly intelligent life have probably been around and living in a harmonic, healthy way for many millions of years. I regard this as a high probability. And they almost certainly differ physically and in many other ways from ourselves.

These two facts render it likely, to judge from our immediate past performance, that upon encountering them, our Government will immediately convene a committee in order to determine whether these creatures constitute a threat to democracy. Since their physical appearance will be markedly different and since difference is usually equated in our culture with inferiority, no matter what the intellectual status of these creatures may be, and regardless of the healthy ways of life that characterize them, we shall, of course, know exactly where we belong in the nature of things. We may even find that instead of electing their politicians by a show of hands, they resort to such subversive activities as requiring all candidates to be not only knowledgeable but also loving beings, who are appointed to office only after they have passed the most rigorous of examinations. In short, we would really have rather a problem on our hands, but we would not want, I suppose, the American way of life to be contaminated. With the record we have of treatment of the American Indians, the blacks, the Chicanos, and other minority groups, and our record in such places as Mexico, the Philippines, China, Vietnam, and wherever else we have attempted to make the world safe for democracy, you can foresee what is likely to happen.

I hope you will understand that the assignment I was given was worded in the form, "How might human beings react to the discovery of life beyond Earth?" and I have interpreted the word "might" to mean "how may we probably react" and "how should we react." We are coming to the "should."

Now, all these and more are possible ways in which we might react to the "beyond-Earthers." Another way in which we might react more creatively and more healthily is by not reacting at all, but by responding with every possible token of interest and friendship. Here at once the problem of communication presents itself. We shall have to work out a mutually intelligible language. With the resources at our mutual disposal, this should not be insuperably difficult.

But it is the communication we make at our initial encounter that is crucial. For this I would suggest that no governmental official be permitted to participate in any way, not even as an observer. The face can be an index to the mind and I would not want our beyond-Earthers to get the wrong idea from the expressions that some of our officials habitually wear, or conversely, to find that there is much less there than meets the eye. So I would suggest that independent bodies be set up outside governmental auspices, outside the United Nations, operating possibly within or in association with a university, whose object shall be to design possible means of establishing frank and friendly communicative relations with beyond-Earthers.

AND THE MIND OF MAN

I do not think we should wait until the encounter occurs; we should do all in our power to prepare ourselves for it. The manner in which we first meet may determine the character of all our subsequent relations. Let us never forget the fatal impact we have had upon innumerable peoples on this Earth—peoples of our own species who trusted us, befriended us, and whom we destroyed by our thoughtlessness and insensitivity to their needs and vulnerabilities.

The simple truth is that before we can communicate with others successfully, we must first learn to communicate with ourselves successfully, and we are a long way from having achieved that. Perhaps that is where we ought to begin—with ourselves. Learning to communicate with ourselves, with all the different peoples and nations of the Earth. This would undoubtedly constitute a first step in learning to communicate with beyond-Earthers. We go on behaving as if we believe there is very little wrong, if anything, with ourselves. We refuse to face the fact that we have already virtually destroyed ourselves as humane beings, and if we recognize any destruction at all, it is that of our environment. We must recognize that we are suffering from a sickness even though it has been repeatedly denied; nevertheless it is, from my point of view as a student of human nature, a fact that most people are no longer humane beings, but sick persons—a sickness induced by the worship of false values, which have corrupted the spirit of man and made him the most dangerous creature on this Earth. Unless he cures himself of this sickness, can one reasonably expect such a creature to behave in a healthy manner? What one can expect him to do is to behave destructively, and a good deal of the time to be unaware of the fact that he is doing so.

Hence, to the question, "How might human beings react to the discovery of life beyond Earth?" I would answer: "Don't wait until that life is discovered, but prepare yourselves for the discovery by becoming what you ought to be, by realizing your evolutionary destiny, which is to live as if to live and to love were one." And what is love? It is the ability to confer survival benefits in a creatively enlarging manner upon the other. And what is health? It is the ability to love, to work, and to play. If we will begin on such a program of rehabilitation, we may be able to respond to the discovery of life beyond Earth in an enhancing manner.

AND THE MIND OF MAN

We have landed on the Moon. It might not be such a bad idea if we tried landing on Earth. When asked by a European inquirer what he thought of Western civilization, Gandhi paused a while, and wryly smiling, replied, "I don't think it would be such a bad idea."

Stendahl

When I think as a theologian on the possibilities of life beyond Earth and even communication with such life, my first reaction is, "That's great!" It seems always great, to me, when God's world gets a little bigger and when I get a somewhat more true view of my place and my smallness in that universe.

In a way, you could say that if there are any people who have intellectually and emotionally trained themselves for dealing with life beyond Earth, I guess they would be the theologians, with their angels and archangels and all the company of Heaven. I am not meaning that in a simple and facetious way. I have often said, and in some of the books that I dutifully read in preparation for this great occasion it is rightfully said, that religious myths and dogmas have held back the mighty development of science. One of the difficulties has been to overcome such systems. I think it is worth noting that that is true when the direct religious instinct and genuine piety of women and men have become amalgamated with certain philosophical systems. I have studied very carefully the way in which the Christian church has lived with changed world views, from a near-Eastern view to the Ptolemaic view to the Copernican view, etc. The real hardcore resistance has usually been lying in those philosophical systems with which they became amalgamated. Plato's old hangup that the circle is perfect and hence everything that is perfect has to be thought of in terms of circles had an enormous influence on the holdback of the development of astronomy. It can be argued very well that any breakthrough of genuine religious insight usually takes the scientific-world view of that time for granted. And you would never hear a Jesus or a Buddha or a Mohammed criticizing the scientific-world view of their time. They take for granted the world view of their time, usually on a very popular level, because that is the way most of us live unless we are specialists in the field.

From a religious point of view, it is very important to keep in mind the specific topic we have before us as a truly enlarging, fascinating, and positive piece of input, raising our cosmic consciousness. I find it especially important for theologians, particularly for theologians and religious people in the Jewish, Christian, and Islamic sects, because, due to certain things that easily happen, one of the great dangers of theology and of the faith is what learned people call "anthropomorphism"—the picturing of God and the universe in too naively human terms. It can be very beautiful, as in Martin Buber's "I and Thou" speculations; but that person was right who, upon returning from Heaven and seeing God, said, "She is Black." That's good theology. And it might be even more significant to break out of the anthropomorphic mode of feeling, singing, and experiencing God. In a way, that was what the old church fathers tried to do with that enormously complex ternary speculation; that was, in a way, what has always been going on at the heart, not only of theology but also of mystical experience—an exploding of a style of behavior as if everything was by the measure and image of man. And in that sense, also a growing cosmic consciousness, or an awareness among human beings like us, of our place in time and space, of our more relative uniqueness rather than absolute uniqueness.

To achieve this by a growing awareness—which I do not find at all threatening as George Wald does—an awareness that really sinks in, that irrespective of the question of communication, it is highly probable that we are only one of numerous possible civilizations—for that to really sink in, for man to really become a part of cosmos in his consciousness, is a great achievement. And it is a kind of recapturing that whole perspective for which so much of theology stands. It is not that we now can prove that the cosmos is filled with beings, that is uninteresting; what is interesting for man is to know both his importance and that this importance should not be built up on the basis of illusions of uniqueness and absoluteness. To me that is important. And hence I am excited in listening, and I am excited in learning.

I have only two final comments. One is that if we translated this into not a panel discussion but into a request for funds, there would be a serious question of priorities. We are dealing here with things that presumably will be enormously expensive. Glamour has something to do with the access to funds, and here I have hesitations, not as to the importance of knowing but as to the speed by

AND THE MIND OF MAN

GREAT GALAXY IN ANDROMEDA (M31). SATELLITE GAL-
AXIES NGC 205 AND 221 ARE ALSO SHOWN. THE PHOTO-
GRAPH WAS TAKEN WITH THE 48-INCH SCHMIDT TELE-
SCOPE. (A HALE OBSERVATORIES PHOTO.)

which we up the cost for such knowing and the way in which we sort our priorities. On that one I guess I would come closer to George Wald, if we looked at it from that point of view. But that is a practical question. That is a human question of priorities. The growing awareness of cosmic cohabitation is enormously important for me, and it fits well into a growing knowledge of God's world.

The final thing I would like to say, somewhat in relation to what Montagu said, is that the tragic image of man, with which I am well familiar theologically and by experience, has something to do with fear. It seems to me that when man is afraid, he is a very vicious being. Much of evilness lies in fear, and that is why increased knowledge is not only an interesting thing but is also a road toward learning both what not to fear and what to fear. That should be kept in mind as we look toward new knowledge in this field.

Morrison

I suppose if you were to ask what instrument would be the most appropriate to the announced topic, you surely would say people are going to talk about what they see through a telescope. But, in fact, at least most of the speakers have really spoken on the topic of what they see in a mirror. Now that is not in any way wrong. Perhaps the most valuable part of this extraordinary enterprise is going to be the mirror with which we confront ourselves obliquely, and in other ways, as we try to ask the question of what the future will be like, of how we are going to get over ourselves to reach that future, and so on. So I am not prepared to say that this is wrong. But as a somewhat matter-of-fact discussant, I am inclined to direct some attention to what I think it really will be like, and not to these mirrorlike discussions, even though they are undoubtedly more important in our present state of mind. Let us take a calmer look at what the real situation is.

Professor Wald, for example, defending magnifi-
cently the creativity of which he is one of the great
pillars of our time, feels that if someone would tell
him the answer, it would be a kind of cheating.
And Dr. Montagu, on the other hand, is quite concerned lest we bring physical and mental harm to
those beings whom we might hypothetically contact. If I were a debater, I would argue that these
two positions would cancel each other out; it can
hardly be both ways.

In fact, I think the situation needs a little clarifi-
cation, and I cannot say that what I am going to
argue is necessarily correct; it is only probable.
You recognize we do not know this field, as Carl
Sagan began by saying. Many surprises, even the
most extraordinary surprises, are possible. It is conceivable that a spherical ship will land in front of
the Washington Monument and a figure with four
antennas and otherwise looking like a professional
football player will rush out and demand to see our
leader. But I hope very much that the universe of
circumstance is wider than the rather shoddy imagi-
nations of science-fiction writers during the past 30
or 40 years. I am pretty well convinced it is. We
have not found their guidance so great in any but

the most modest activities, like going to the Moon. Science fiction of a hundred years ago told us how to go to the Moon, and we have done that.

I think, on the contrary, that an enormous distance separates us from the nearest existing group of a similar kind. And it is truly an enormous distance—not the distance to the Moon, not the distance to the planets, not the distance to the nearest stars, but tens or even hundreds or perhaps thousands of times that distance. That means that even by traveling at the speed of light, no round trip is likely to be imaginable, and communications would be extremely difficult. They say, "Hello!" You say, "How are you?" And they say, "Fine." That conversation will take at least centuries. And I really do not think that that is going to bring us into conflict with the problems of the day. It may bring us near problems of some other day, but I am unable to see far enough into the future to notice how our little, not petty, but tragic circumstances of contemporary history are going to affect that.

Nor do I think this communication can be by any other means than light, or its cognate, radio. The universe is simply too great for other means. The cost of getting enough energy to make physical

A CLUSTER OF GALAXIES IN HERCULES TAKEN WITH THE 200-INCH TELESCOPE. (A HALE OBSERVATORIES PHOTO.)

AND THE MIND OF MAN

travel possible is overwhelming, even for civilizations with enormous means, far beyond our own. It is conceivable that after a long time of exchange of knowledge, a ceremonial visit might be made. I can understand that. Everybody makes a great effort and finally come together. But that would not be the initial stage, and would not occur for a long time, until enormous rapport had built up. A time measured not in presidentiads, mind you, but in lifetimes of the republic; that is to say, in spans of 100 or 200 years.

So I do not think we are talking about just a normal enterprise; we are talking about an enterprise more like the development of agriculture than even like the discovery of America. The discovery of America looks to us like a sudden event, but from 1492 until 1605, nobody came to New England. And that is a long time, nearly as long as the time since the War of 1812. So we truncate history. Sometimes we think things happen in a snap, but they do not. They happen very slowly.

I think, therefore, that we will get a message, but it will not be simple. I would like to discuss the message itself for a few minutes to give a feeling of what I think is one possible model. The only way, I think, to achieve success in these matters is to invent models and schemes, not because any of them are necessarily right, but because in this way we mirror what the technical people will have to examine to see how we might get this thing done. Also, others will have to tell us the meaning of it, what will come of it. You have got to ask what might actually happen; then, in the light of that, prepare to meet those circumstances. If you are wrong, as you undoubtedly will be, you will have prepared something quite interesting and flexible, which is probably closer to the real event, although not very close, than you would be in the absence of any preparation.

I think there will be two great phases of this eventual time—which will come (perhaps in ten years, or a hundred, or maybe longer)—when some satisfactory radio-telescope work or something similar will acquire evidence of the deliberate beaming of a protracted message from space. First, the most important issue is the recognition of the message. Just that it is there, not what it says. This is often technically called the "acquisition" of the message. There will, of course, be false starts. There will be many claims. There have already been claims—I think rather facetious ones. They turned out to be wrong. I believe that will happen a number of times—three times, ten times, many times. It will continue until we have got something that cannot be anything else save a message.

I think, on the other hand, that when we do acquire this message, in the right way, it will be unmistakable; for example, it will take a week of verification to make sure that the statements are really true, but once that happens it will be so clear that the signal is something vastly different from the complex natural phenomena we know already that nobody will doubt it. I think this is true, just as nobody doubts if you find a Phidias or a Greek vase in the ground. Maybe you argue about how it got there. Maybe you argue if a pebble was really hammered; but these are only early stages in the making of tools. But the message will not be that way at all. It will be an elaborately planned, very great social effort on the part of some distant society. So I think that it will be easy to authenticate, and, of course, the message will be extraordinarily important.

At first you will know very little of what that message says, save that it exists, and maybe some general information about its source—how far away it is, what kind of a star and where. And then, I think, you will have pouring into the radio telescope's recorders, week after week, month after month, decade after decade, an enormous body of obviously interesting and meaningful postals. You will be able to read them, slowly and fitfully, because they will not be coded but anticoded; that is, the beings who designed them will have thought very carefully how to make the maximum number of mathematical clues so that the meaning will be clear. And it will be a large volume of material; it will not be something that the *New York Times* will publish in its entirety. It will be too voluminous, too technical, too uncertain, too much in need of study.

The closest analogy I can use is the enormous impact on modern thought (post-Renaissance European thought) of the Greek world. As a body of material it can be summed up in about 10 000 books. We have only about 10 000 books written from Hesiod to Hero down to the Alexandrians. Every decade or so someone will perhaps find another one buried in a backyard in Alexandria or in the Middle East, but no substantial number will be added. We can never interrogate any playwright, philosopher, or physicist from Hellenic times, and ask him what he meant by his statements. Yet the body of material from that period has been of great importance to the forming of the whole mind of our time. But not because everybody in the street reads it. I think it is fair to say, with Professor Montagu, that that will not be the way it will happen. It has influence because the people who write the books we do read have read it; and the students in the universities come to grips with it, and it informs and stimulates artists, scientists, poets, historians. With the discovery of the message, such a body of literature and technology and science and question answering and the rest will come, I think, every year. A mass of 10 000 books every year.

But it will come with extraordinary differences, so great we can hardly imagine how great they are. First, the people who send it will be incredibly alien. Even if their biochemistry resembles what Professor Wald teaches, it will not be all that close, you know. You could not eat their food, very likely, even if you have the same biochemistry, anymore than you can eat the food of a mushroom; it is very difficult to eat that. But meaning will slowly come out of this study, and it will contain, for better or worse, the answer to many questions that we cannot ourselves answer, which we will have to debate and interpret and work on and test. The successors of Professor Wald will still be studying whether what they say could really be right.

I think the most important thing the message will bring us, if we can finally understand it, will be a description, if one exists at all, of how these beings were able to fashion a world in which they could live, persevere, and maintain something of worth and beauty for a long period of time. Again, we will not be able to translate it directly and make our institutions like theirs; the circumstance will be too different. But something of it will come through in this way. I think, therefore, that this will be the most important message we could receive. But it will be more of a subtle, long-lasting, complex, debatable effect than a sudden revelation of truth, like letters written in fire in the sky.

So I am neither fearful nor terribly expectant. I am anxious for that first acquisition, to make sure that we are not alone. But once that is gained—it might be gained in my lifetime—then I think we can rest with some patience to see what complexities have turned up on other planets. And if after considerable search we do not find that our counterparts exist somewhere else, I cannot think that would be wrong either, because that would give us even a heavier responsibility to represent intelligence in this extraordinarily large and diverse universe.

Berendzen

Some comments before we open for free discussion.

Dr. Stendahl mentioned the question of costs. As a matter of factual information, in 1971 a design study of a system for picking up interstellar communication was made in California by several radio-scientists, astronomers, and others. It was called Project Cyclops.* The outcome of that study was that the United States had the technical capability of building a large radio array, which would be able to scan the heavens with adequately great resolution and sensitivity to detect signals from many hundreds or possibly thousands of light-years away. It would have the distinct possibility of picking up signals if they are there. Although the authors of the report argued eloquently that the search would be worthwhile, the cost could run on the order of $6 to $10 billion over a 10- to 15-year

---

* Copies of the final report of Project Cyclops can be obtained from Dr. John Billingham, NASA/Ames Research Center, Code LT, Moffett Field, Calif. 94035.

period. This project has not been undertaken, but it is worth knowing that such a feasibility study has been made.

It should be noted, nevertheless, that whether you intentionally wish to communicate or not, there is at least some chance that the discovery could be made by accident, simply by using the radio telescopes we already have. But, as Phil Morrison pointed out years ago, the chances of finding the radio signals by accident is fairly low unless you just happen to look toward the right star at the right epoch in the right wavelength band.

Dr. Wald mentioned a number of reasons why he was fearful about the possibility of making contact. In line with arguments in the Cyclops report, let me summarize very briefly some of the reasons why we might want to make a search and some why we might not. I hope the other panelists will respond to these.

Why might we want to make the search? For one thing, it could contribute to the continuing adventure of exploration. Within the next few decades we will have explored most of our "ghetto Earth," as our planet might be viewed in its present state of cosmic quarantine. We are now expanding into the solar system, but there is an enormity of space. And one might ask the social scientists if the inquisitive mind of man will be satisfied to be limited over astronomical time periods to his own minute locale.

Second, consider biochemistry. Surely, the possibilities of learning new facts in biochemistry would be truly outstanding. It could be true, perhaps, that that "instant knowledge" would rob us of the benefits of our own inquisitiveness. On the other hand, the person who has cancer would not care whether the discovery of its cure came from the Boston Medical Center or from Tau Ceti.

And finally, it would perhaps provide us with the opportunity of joining what has been called the "galactic heritage." Let us move beyond the obvious, trite matters of scientific or technological gain that contact might provide. It might also lead us to better social forms, possibly to ways to solve our environmental crises, and even improve our own social institutions. If these civilizations have been able to survive for thousands or tens of thousands of years, perhaps they could tell us how in their infancy they had been able to overcome these problems. Their very being would constitute an existence proof that such problems are not inevitably debilitating. Perhaps they could even tell us about new esthetic forms, which would raise our consciousness, making life more enjoyable and rewarding. Thus the benefits could come not merely in terms of technology and science, but also in the arts, literature, and humanities. And beyond that —and probably the most significant of all—contact would end our social and cultural isolation. To date, we have been bound not only into our own countries and small, artificial zones on this planet, but most assuredly within the solar system itself. If there are the millions of other civilizations that the predictions indicate might exist, then we would join a larger galactic community. Now, at last, we may be on the verge of reaching young cosmic adulthood. This astronomical perspective of history is instructive, just in itself; but it may also indicate to us the ultimate meaning of achieving interstellar contact.

On the other hand, there are potential hazards. For example, there is the possibility, often mentioned in science fiction, of invasion. But as many of the panelists have noted, interstellar space travel seems to be improbable. The distances appear too vast and the energy requirements too great, limitations not set by our level of technology but apparently by Nature itself. Perhaps we should not be overly concerned about an eventuality that seems, by even radical extrapolations of contemporary science, to be so unlikely.

There is the possibility of exploitation, again repeatedly voiced in science fiction, where the creatures covet our goods. It would be hard to imagine, however, exactly what they would want here. Their biochemistry would be so different that they probable could not use our air or food or other natural resources. These things that seem precious to us would most likely not be precious to them. Ours is but one of a multitude of planets in the universe, many of which must contain the same elements as the Earth; in short, there is nothing unique about the composition of our home. These other places, therefore, would be equally suitable for the beings, without requiring them to make an inordinately long space trip. But, of course, this exercise amounts to trying to guess the motivations of totally alien, hypothetical beings.

There is also the possibility of subversion, in which they would tell us interesting things by means of radio communication, but for devious, ill reasons they would intentionally lead us astray. I would like to ask the anthropologist about the evidence here on Earth of advanced societies subverting less-advanced ones in this way. Is this a generic problem?

And finally, we come to cultural shock. George Wald has already alluded to this. But how much cultural shock can you achieve by radio communication? If the first contact is simply a statement of "Hi, I'm here," and then many hundreds of years later information begins to trickle in, which undoubtedly would take tens or hundreds of years to decipher, there is a real question to me of how much cultural shock that would bring. Just the realization that we are not alone could be traumatic, but would it threaten our egos, shatter our institutions, destroy our lives?

These are only a few of the issues at hand. To give the other speakers time, I will stop here and ask Carl Sagan to start the response, because he spoke first. Then the rest of the panel should join in freely.

Sagan

There is a very rich and diverse array of opinions before us. I would like to comment on a few of them that struck me as particularly interesting.

On the question of costs, I would just like to set a few contexts. It is true that the scheme proposed in the study Project Cyclops—there is no such instrument—would cost several billions of dollars. But such a radio telescope would be designed not for listening for a signal beamed at us, but for eavesdropping on communications among planets of other stars. It would amount to listening in on their domestic radio traffic, late-afternoon television, and so on. That clearly is the thing you do after you fail to get a message directly beamed at you.

What would be the cost of construction of a radio telescope to be used, say, half or full time for communication with extraterrestrial intelligence, including maintenance expenses, over a period of some decades? (A few decades are necessary because that is how long it would take to search the nearest 100,000 or so stars adequately, which is roughly the number you have to run through according to even some of the more optimistic assumptions before you come upon one such civilization.) What is the cost of one such enterprise? It comes to 1 day of the Vietnam war! That seems to me a comparison which does not lead us to conclude that such an enterprise is excessively costly.

To go to the other end, another aspect of this question is the exploration of our solar system by unmanned spacecraft. That is important for finding out if there are simple forms of life on, say, Mars or Jupiter. If the answer to that were yes, then the likelihood of the origin of life on planets of other stars would naturally be vastly greater. Imagine a program of unmanned exploration of the entire solar system for the decade of the 1970's which would examine every planet, and would land several space vehicles on the surface of Mars. What would such a program cost? Such a program would cost less than the 1970 fiscal year cost overrun on the anti-ballistic-missile system. To put that in another way, the cost-forecasting errors on a single weapons system come to more than a decade's ex-

AND THE MIND OF MAN

ploration of the entire solar system. So again, it strikes me that this Nation has the resources to undertake such exploratory ventures, and certainly this planet has those resources. It is just a question of, Do we wish to do it?

Now there is a second thing I would like to pick up. I view the problem very much as Philip Morrison does, and I very strongly agree that the question becomes a kind of psychological projective test. People see in this issue of is-there-life-out-there-and-what-should-we-do-about-it the reflection of their own hopes and fears and even unspoken, unconscious processes. When we sent the plaque out on Pioneer 10, we got a quite remarkable sampling of global opinion on subjects that had not crossed our mind at all in designing it. Let me give you some flavor of this. We got some angry letters from people who objected to sending smut to the stars. There was a letter in the *Los Angeles Times* which said, "Isn't it bad enough we are spreading pornography all over America; now we have to send it up into the sky, and corrupt the guys out there." A week later there was a response to that which went something like this. "I agree with those people who think we shouldn't be sending all those

55

dirty pictures into space. What we should have done is visually bleep out the reproductive organs of the man and woman, and instead show a stork carrying its little bundle from heaven." Then the letter went on to say that to further inform the extraterrestrials about the level of cultural advance on the Earth, we should include pictures of Santa Claus, the Easter Bunny, and the Tooth Fairy. This is just one category of hangup that the plaque exposed. There are about 10 or 12 other major kinds of social anxieties that this plaque evoked responses on. I think all of us are going to have the difficulty of not being able to transcend the problems of our times, the problems of ourselves, in viewing the subject. We have to do the best we can.

The final remark that I want to make right now is to respond more directly to a few of the remarks of George Wald and Ashley Montagu. George Wald has made a statement that I have applauded many times, which I am now giving from memory, but it goes something like, "What is needed is a generally accepted cosmic context for mankind." And I think what George was talking about, surely what I talk about when I say a thing like that, is that the old secure sense of where we are in the universe has eroded. It has eroded because the traditional world views have faced unsuccessful contact with the real world, and those old-world views have not been replaced by a similarly comfortable and acceptable view of where we are, where we have come from, where we are likely to be going, and who else there is around. That was all very tidily in hand a few hundred years ago; it is not tidily in hand right now. It is very messy right now. And that is because we are at a remarkable, evolutionary point in the history of mankind. The kind of exploratory ventures we are talking about seem to me to be precisely the kind that are needed to reestablish a cosmic context for mankind. By finding out what the other planets are like—by finding out whether there are civilizations on planets of other stars—we reestablish a context for ourselves.

Montagu was concerned about differences being equated with inferiorities, which is surely one of the tragic circumstances of mankind. But it seems to me the search for extraterrestrial intelligence precisely *undoes* that concern. Because the one clear lesson from evolution that I think all panelists have agreed upon is that those guys out there may be smarter than us, but they are not human beings.

Human beings are the product of a particular, exquisitely difficult evolutionary pathway that happened on Earth once and will never occur anywhere else again. Therefore, when we make contact with beings very different from us who are in many contexts superior to us, those old prejudices that have plagued mankind for thousands of years, must, it seems to me, fall by the boards. There may be insecurities about our not being at the pinnacle of creation, but those kinds of problems do not worry me nearly as much as the kind to which Dr. Montagu alluded. I think that once this idea of there being one tiny planet, which has on it human beings who do not exist anywhere else—once that idea pervades the general thinking of the mass of mankind—then the brotherhood of human beings stands out in crystal clarity. Therefore, the search for extraterrestrial intelligence, much less the successful search, has a vital role to play in how we view ourselves and our neighbors.

Wald

I wonder if I could get into this again, because I would hate to be misunderstood as trying to limit

58

AND THE MIND OF MAN

our knowledge in any sense, being afraid of learning anything. The difficulty is somewhere else. It is in that strange territory that is so all-important now —the distinction between science, which is knowing, and technology, which is application. To put it in a simple phrase, I would say my own position is: "Know all you can, but do only those things that it is socially useful to do."

And that is really our problem. If one could get a definite answer to whether there are indeed more advanced civilizations and technologies in outer space, I should be happy to have that answer, as with those of all other such questions. I do not, as I have said, look forward to the possibility of some continuous transmission that might completely supersede all further human efforts in the direction of hard-won creative understanding. Furthermore, I am not really made comfortable in that thought by what Phil Morrison has said about its being difficult and taking a lot of time. That is just again those few elite persons who are listening to our end of the transmission. That will be their thing. *They'll* have an interesting time. *They'll* have good jobs. *They'll* have high status. It's the rest of mankind that I worry about.

Morrison

What is there to worry about, George? What is going to happen when these books are printed?

Wald

Oh, I think a degree of degradation of the human enterprise. What are you going to do when all the things that make you proud and think it worthy to be a man are demonstrated to be unimaginably inferior to what creatures out there know and do? It has been well said here: We are the only *men* in the universe. I am about as sure of that as I am of anything. Krister thinks as a theologian, "Why, it's wonderful because we'll see the wider province of God." How do dogs feel about your God, Krister? Are they proud, you know, of being men's dogs, and having a dog's share of man's God? You see, I think we are in a real bind.

(Krister Standahl, as you have been told, is the Dean of the Harvard Divinity School. I was working for him this morning and yesterday morning and he does not even know it. I gave 6-minute sermons in the Harvard Chapel yesterday morning and this morning, and what I was talking about in part is just this question.)

You see, I think we're facing a new parochialism. The Judeo-Christian concept of God is itself highly parochial even on this planet. There are and always have been other gods on this planet; yet we like to think of our god as a God of this planet. We even claim for Him a status in the universe without asking elsewhere. That would be an interesting question to ask, if one ever established that transmission.

But, you see, I think our home in space is the solar system; and since humbleness is the vogue in religion, I would be so humble as to think that those who have a belief in God might believe in Him as the God of the solar system. The other thought, that He's the God of the universe, is obviously conceivable, but to me it is rather comic.

Montagu

May I reply to Carl Sagan's questions? First, about the necessity of continuing scientific exploration. At one time I subscribed to the idea as a scientist that,

of course, science should be free and open and continuously explorative. I no longer subscribe to that
dictum. I do not think that further scientific discovery and technological application of those discover-
ies remains an inviolable principle. As George
Wald pointed out, certainly let us increase our
knowledge—let us remain continuously curious and
explorative—but also, at the same time, let us remain explorative of the means by which we can
control the application of our knowledge. This is
where we have, I think, lamentably failed.

Another point that Carl Sagan raised was that
perhaps we could learn from these extraterrestrial
civilizations something about how to behave on
Earth as human beings. Well, as an anthropologist,
may I point out that we have had on Earth civilizations which we have exterminated from which we
could have learned an enormous amount about
how to behave as human beings. We still have
about a dozen of these societies—like the Anda-
man Islanders, the Kalahari bushmen, a few rem-
nants of the Australian aborigines, the Semai of
Malaya, and the Eskimo—all of whom we are very
busily engaged in destroying, but not learning
anything from, because we approach them with at-

titudes which are so destructive. Namely, that we are the superior cultures and they are the primitive cultures. So if we cannot learn from peoples on Earth, it is very improbable that we are likely to learn anything from people who are on other planets.

Sagan

There seem to be two differences between the monstrous chronicle of the contact between the so-called advanced and so-called primitive civilizations on the Earth and the situation we are imagining. First of all, the guys we contact have to be more advanced than we. I say "have to be," because anybody dumber than us has not yet developed radio technology, and so we cannot talk to those guys at all. In fact, there is almost certainly no civilization in the galaxy dumber than us that we can talk to. We are the dumbest communicative civilization in the galaxy. We are very much the low man on the exploitation totem pole, so I cannot get exercised at all about us destroying some of those other guys.

Nor can I get much worked up about the opposite possibility for a different reason—namely, the kind of cosmic quarantine established by the immense distances between the stars. As several people have mentioned, it not only means that physical travel is exceedingly difficult, but even little communications by radio are exceedingly sluggish. The scenario that Philip Morrison talked about— "Hello, how are you?" "Fine."—takes 600 years. That is not what you might call a snappy conversation! For that reason, it just does not worry me at all in this context that we have this abysmal history of wiping out other civilizations from whom we could have learned a lot. What I am imagining is that when the facts I have just stated become generally known, people will know that there are a million other civilizations, all fabulously ugly, and all a lot smarter than us. Knowing this seems to me to be a useful and character-building experience for mankind.

The other point I wanted to get back to is this. George, I still cannot understand what worries you. I quite agree that it is important to control the products of technology; that we should not have every conceivable technological opportunity pursued, because some technology is bad and some technology is good. I quite agree with that, but I do not see how it appears in this issue at all. The thing I have been trying to wrestle with since 10 years ago when we had a similar discussion is: Imagine the situation of information coming in on vitamin A, or whatever it is that you are working on, and you find they beat you to it. So what? I try to imagine back to when I was working hard as a student. There were a lot of textbooks. I would open up those textbooks and in there would be what other guys had found out. Now I did not approach each phase saying, "Oh, my God! They know that also!"

Wald

May I reply to that one? You see, this is a beautiful exposition of the myths we live with. One of those myths is that what happens, happens on the basis of the best information. That is not the world we are in at all. We are in a great world crisis now, and it is not a crisis of information—it is a crisis of decision, it is a crisis of policy. There is no major problem that is facing the world today—the population explosion, the possibility of nuclear warfare, pollution—that we have not sufficient information to move in on at once and act upon. But we are not doing any of those things. There is not one major threat among the many that are facing us that we do not know how to begin to handle. But they are not being handled; we have not even begun to handle them. And incidentally may I say that there is not one of them that can be handled while maximizing profits.

Do you want to find out about other ways to live? Why are not we carefully exploring how the Chinese are living? You figure that one out! Why is it not that all of us who are so eager to learn new things are not eagerly examining, with our Government taking the forefront in that job, how the Chinese are managing. You do not have to go to outer space for new information; but our crisis is not an information crisis.

Let me, before stopping, give you an example of what I am talking about, because Carl Sagan, who is an exceedingly bright guy, and talks so nicely, asks "What am I afraid of?" He does not disagree with me that applications of technology need to be controlled. *Are* they being controlled? Does it bother him that that is the last thing that is happening now?

AND THE MIND OF MAN

Let me go into a bit of biochemistry that is cosmic in its magnitude. You see, the biggest event in the evolution of life on this planet—no doubt about it—was the development of photosynthesis. Why? Because with photosynthesis, life solved the problem of keeping itself going indefinitely. Because after having to live before on the age-old accumulation of organic matter during the billion years or so before life arose on Earth, we now could make our own organic matter, using the energy of sunlight—it was a big deal! It made us independent of our heritage of organic matter.

Only a little over 25 years ago, what could well have been the second biggest event in the evolution of life on this planet occurred, with the first access to nuclear energy. All life on this Earth runs ultimately on sunlight. If we could just solve the problem of performing a controlled thermonuclear reaction—that is what makes sunlight—it would, in a sense, bring sunlight into our own hands, and within our own control. Life on Earth would thereby become to a degree independent of sunlight. Yet that marvelous opportunity has come to us in the form of an explosion. Stockpiles of hydrogen bombs are now threatening our lives. We are living in a balance of terror. And that epic event that opened an enormous new hope for life on the Earth—the second biggest event in its development—appeared in the form of the bombing of Hiroshima and Nagasaki. So do not agree with me, Carl Sagan, that "Yes, indeed, we all agree that technology needs to be controlled"—let us try to start controlling it.

Morrison

George, very few people disagree with you on that point; it is a very important problem. But nothing in life has ever come easily, including the development of ideas or technology. To use the great metaphor, throughout time men have had to earn their bread by sweat and women to bring forth children by labor. I do not think we will ever be without difficulties, without failures.

I cannot think the best answer is to say, "It's too bad there are atoms because then we are going to be able to exploit them." If there is life out there, sooner or later we are going to find it, or it will find us. I do not think you can avoid it, George. The truth will, in a way, come out.

AND THE MIND OF MAN

Stendahl

I was going to raise the question of priorities. But there is another aspect which we have touched on here which is: What do people get fascinated by, and when do you get certain things going? It is a sad fact that it is easier to do things for war than peace. We know that, and in that lies the real tragedy of the situation. What I hear Montagu and Wald speak about is not just dollars, but: Why is it that we cannot raise the level of—let me use the word—"fascination" with the problems of the kind which Montagu and Wald have raised. I think there is a fear, a valid fear, that interstellar communication has such glamour in it that one wants to speak out against everyone saying, "Yes, that is enormous, that's wonderful, that's great."

I find our chairman perhaps overstating it, or perhaps he is not, when he sort of comes back to this, saying that they will tell us about cancer and this and that. If I read the signs right, that is so distant and improbable that it is not the point. And even others having one-upmanship on us in intelligence is also not the point. That is when I say, "So what!"

I have two more comments. I do not want to discuss theology with George Wald before you all here. I just want to say one thing, and I hope to say it without sounding wrong. For him who somehow believes in God, God is never a concept; but He definitely transcends that concept. I know, I think, even more than George Wald does about all kinds of wicked limitations and suppressions and evil things in various concepts of God. But I also know that for believers it is always right to say that those are petty concepts and God is something bigger. I am very much concerned about this. I really think that it is not as simple as saying that man created a concept of God and where does the dog fit into it. If you mean God when you say God, you might even in the long run have to reorganize your behavior to dogs. I do not want to belabor that, but I want to identify a *concept* of God with what I am concerned about here—namely, a really exploded cosmic consciousness, as I see really coming out of that first message. I am much more interested in that first message—the fact that the message is there—than I am in getting one-up on various problems, because it has to do with the total view of the world in which we live.

AND THE MIND OF MAN

I have one final question I have to ask Ashley Montagu. He has said so many things tongue in cheek, so I do not know on what level to listen to him. But he did suggest that the solution—and I want just to be sure whether this was irony or true —that the way to prepare for the Great Day was to not allow the government to participate, but that it should be done within a university. My trust, perhaps especially as a dean of a faculty within a university, does not give me that enormous confidence in universities. I just want to know where you were on this one.

Montagu

I want to assure Professor Stendahl that I did not have my tongue in my cheek at all; I meant every word that I said, and if irony was there, it was like a cheerfulness which could not help creeping in. And in connection with universities, with which I have spent the greater part of my life, I thoroughly agree with Professor Stendahl's evaluation of them, so succinctly and beautifully put.

I said: "Certainly exclude all government and governmental officials and agencies; and, at most, establish it either in association with a university or within a university—implying there that one would carefully choose the university, if such a university exists. . . ."

And I would suggest that if we are to make any progress in human relations, we had better study those people whom I regard as really advanced— not the people on other planets in other galaxies, but rather the people (and this remark is addressed with due respect to you, Carl) who one calls "primitive." There are no primitive peoples, except in technology. They are vastly more advanced in the way in which they are able to relate themselves. We have lost this because we have become agriculturalized and urbanized and have been descending in the direction so beautifully described by a New York high school girl when she was asked to write a paper on the evolution of man. She began it by saying that man is descended from the apes and has been descending ever since.

Stendahl

May I just say one thing on that? Why I did not like your comment was that the problems ahead of

us are too great, too difficult, so that any kind of
uptightness in the university world would be bad;
we should not think that we alone are the ones who
are going to solve the problems of communication
with extraterrestrial life forms.

Montagu

Is it not interesting that many of the great geniuses
of our contemporary world did their work outside
the university?

Berendzen

I think it is worthwhile to note here that Fred
Hoyle, the famous cosmologist, has mentioned that
the single criterion he was positive would be necessary for an intelligent, advanced civilization to exist
elsewhere would be education.

May we now have questions from the floor,
please? They can be addressed to either the entire
panel or individual panelists.

QUESTION

I am interested in what all the members of the panel think about the feasibility and desirability of people living off this planet. What are the consequences for human beings, for the human spirit, of living off the Earth? What kind of educational processes would we need for people to live off the planet? The problems of communication are really inherent just on the panel, let alone talking with other kinds of life.

BERENDZEN

As I understand the question, you are asking primarily about terrestrial beings going somewhere else and living. That is a rather different issue. Would somebody want to respond?

MONTAGU

So far as feasibility is concerned, I understand that this is so astronomically costly as to be out of the question.

As for desirability, as an anthropologist, I would say it is absolutely undesirable. Unless and until we have learned to solve our problems on this Earth, we certainly should not visit them upon any other people.

SAGAN

I quite agree that it would be an extremely expensive undertaking to place colonies of human beings on some other nearby planet. (I am not now talking about planets of other stars.) For that reason I personally would oppose any such venture for the near future, but on a longer timescale I think it is inevitable that human beings will start having colonies on the Moon and on the nearby planets. I personally think on that time scale—the next century or two—it is something very much to be desired. There is a phrase of the Soviet founder of astronautics, Constantin Tsiolkovskii, which I can paraphrase: "The Earth is the cradle of mankind, but one does not live in the cradle forever."

One other remark. You were talking about the difficulties of communication among the panel members, saying that if we could not communicate among ourselves, what chance is there of communicating with somebody else? I would again call your attention to the almost certain fact that those guys out there are going to be smarter than us.

75

WALD

If Carl Sagan had not just spoken, I would not say anything, but now I have to. By "those guys out there," I take it he is talking about places very far away, but I think the question is being asked about the planets of the solar system. So let me give you a very plain answer: There is no place else in the solar system fit for man to live! Do you want to have a big exploration to find some other place to colonize where it is unfit to live? How about the bottom of the sea? Would not that be fun! Let us colonize the bottom of the ocean! As my very wise friend, Lewis Mumford, once said, "There is nothing in all outer space as precious as one acre of the Earth." We're built to live on the Earth. And we can only make these exciting explorations elsewhere in the solar system by carrying our environment along with us. When we have run out of that environment, we have to come home. So far, thank heavens, all the astronauts made it in time.

MORRISON

I would not have engaged either if you had not gone so far . . . Mr. Mumford is a nice man, but he

AND THE MIND OF MAN

is often wrong and he is wrong there, too. The most important part of the solar system—I think you would agree, there is no question about it for man as well as for everybody else—is the Sun. It is not the Earth; it is the Sun. Our knowledge of the behavior of the Sun is indispensable to our continued life on this planet. If there is any place for a manned observation—say from the surface of the Moon or from orbit, which would tell us about solar flares, about ice ages—I think it might be very worth our investing in it. I am not one of those persons who thinks we are going to have colonization in the solar system any more than we have colonization in Antarctica. But we have maintained for 15 or 20 years a quite intrepid, small, permanent scientific meteorological station on Antarctica. It is a hard life. Nobody expects to have anybody living there, but I believe it is a valuable enterprise. It does not cost a lot and it will be one day very valuable. That may well be the case for outer space. It is all very well to talk about a green acre being more valuable. Of course it is. That is putting it in poetic language. You can understand that. I do not think any of us, surely not Carl, is proposing that we should turn the Moon into a Disneyland. That is extraordinarily implausible. But I do not think that means that there is no possible gain for the farmer or the hunter in the plains of the Kalahari in the investigation of space. On the contrary, it is very likely that what we learn there will in the long run be valuable.

BERENDZEN

Even though this matter is vital and interesting, it is off from our basic topic today. An adequate discussion of space exploration might be saved for a future meeting.

QUESTION

I would like to address a question to Philip Morrison. He mentioned that the information would probably come from some sort of compendium, very carefully orchestrated. Assuming that we have no feedback to them, they would not know when to begin this broadcast. I would think it would be more likely that we would tune in on some sort of broadcast in session. How likely is it that we would be getting information that could not be translated without a Rosetta stone?

AND THE MIND OF MAN

MORRISON

You touch exactly on topics that I really was going to discuss if we had not been thrust into a very large, philosophic context, which in many ways is more interesting and probably more suitable for our limited time today. But some of us have thought about how to construct a message of just the kind you say, a message that has a growing and interesting meaning the moment you hear it; then as long as you keep listening to it, you learn more and more and more from it. You do not have to wait to come in at the middle of the chorus. We see that in our own world of newspapers, books, radio stations, and so on; the point is, some things repeat. Very simple stereotyped things, like call signals or the masthead of a newspaper, come out every day. Well, these are not exactly the same, but they are very similar in form. After a few messages you get the general idea. And I think the general message will be like that—mostly repetitive, somewhat stereotyped things, which will help us to learn the language.

First, there will be an acquisition signal. This is really an artificial thing and not something made by a star. Second, there will be the mathematical basis on which you can interpret the symbols, the way to make a language out of the symbols. That will repeat over and over again; and, in between, a lot of stuff we will not read very well will gradually build up into knowledge, probably about how to get better signals and more of them. Then everything else will flow—what they want to say about their culture, or whatever they think will be interesting.

Just as you said, this will be an ongoing message, repeated for thousands and thousands of years without an answer.

It has not perhaps been stressed here today, but it is really a good deal harder to send than to receive, even with the model of Arecibo before us. It takes a lot more effort and money, especially if you do not know just where to send to. Thus I think it is quite likely that we would be incapable of sending a message for a very long time.

QUESTION

Communications between ourselves and other civilizations can be considered in general in two

80

basic categories. One is a sort of passive communication in which we receive information from other beings; we just sit there and compile it and perhaps eventually sort it out. And the other is an active communication, in which we ourselves can try sending signals. And as far as the active part is concerned, the first step ought to be to construct some sort of signal that would be identifiable as to the fact that we were intelligent beings. But beyond that, as Carl Sagan said, these people are a lot more intelligent than we are. The next step would be to send out one piece of information that would characterize our society. Since they are probably more intelligent or advanced than we, deep consideration should be given to just precisely what piece of information should be sent out, because the wrong characterization of our society, or the wrong interpretation of it, could be quite damaging in the long run.

SAGAN

I do not think it is quite as urgent to send as to receive, which may be a paraphrase of a Biblical passage. Also, I again would want to stress that, willy-nilly, we have been sending, so your remarks are most properly directed to the FCC. The image of our society, which is garnered at some place 30 light-years out, is the image you get by turning on the late-night tube. So if you are worried about sending out the wrong message, you have every reason to be worried.

BERENDZEN

Let me mention something that I would hate to pass without adequate discussion. Is it possible that if we detected a signal from space, it would have the dramatic, beneficial effect on mankind of bringing us together?

SAGAN

Well, I alluded to that before. I think chances of that happening are very great, because as soon as it is clear that there is somebody else out there and they are smarter than us and they are different from us, then the differences between the various slight subsets of mankind which people are spending a lot of time worrying about—those differences I think tend to. . . .

AND THE MIND OF MAN

MONTAGU

Look, we have had someone out there for an awfully long time, whom Dr. Stendahl calls "God." I take it he is referring to the Christian God. As an anthropologist I am acquainted with several hundred gods. And this God is supposed to be all-wise and all-loving, etc. We seem to have learned very little from Him. Why should our communication with extraterrestrial beings have a more cohesive effect than the concepts of the Catholic Church, for example?

SAGAN

It is a good question. There are many possible long answers, but maybe the fastest answer I can give is that there may be some room for doubt about the reality of the several hundred gods you were talking about, but once the message is received, I think there will be very little room for doubt about the reality of the message.

MONTAGU

But I do not doubt the existence of any of these hundreds of Gods! I believe anything you believe to be real is as real as it could possibly be, even though it's unreal.

SAGAN

That's why you have such an exemplary moral character!

QUESTION

I would like to ask Sagan and the other members of the panel if there is going to be a Pioneer 11 with a plaque on it. What would Sagan add to or subtract from the earlier plaque if another one is to be made? And what would the other members of the panel urge to put on it or leave off?

SAGAN

This again is the area, as I mentioned before, of the psychological projective test. There is going to be a Pioneer 11, the same kind of mission as Pioneer 10. I have no idea at the present time whether there will be a plaque on it,* and if so,

---

* There will be a plaque on Pioneer G, to be renamed Pioneer 11 after successful launch, and it will be the same as the one on Pioneer 10.—*Editor*.

what its content would be. The essential part of the plaque was the distribution of pulsars, which, I think in a rather nice way, says where we are and when we are. The ambiguous part of the plaque is the representation of the two human beings, which says who we are. We had a representation of a man and woman looking friendly; how much of that gets communicated is, I suspect, very slight. We would be grateful for suggestions on how to do it better. But I think the useful aspect of this, as an earlier question indicated, is that once you start making such messages, you are forced to consider the image of mankind that you would like to project up there. And that is, I think, of much greater significance than the actual sending of the plaque.

MORRISON

Carl, is not the most important message attached to Pioneer 10 the spacecraft itself?

SAGAN

Oh, yes, of course. . . .

MORRISON

It is a far more important, rich, complex message about the nature of mankind than anything you can invent to put on a plaque. You put on some coordinates. That was a very good idea. And beyond that, I really don't know what else you can do.

SAGAN

That is quite right. I can say though that there have been enormous numbers of suggestions. For example, one person said: "Look, here are these line drawings of a man and a woman. The perspectives and conventions of other civilizations are going to be different. Why half measures? Send two cadavers! They can be cold frozen in interstellar space, perfectly preserved. Other creatures can take them apart at their leisure and find out what we are really about. Why line drawings?" So I wrote back saying, well, there were some weight problems. . . .

WALD

I think Carl just said a very important thing, and that is that the telescope *is* a mirror, and one of its more important functions is to hold a mirror to man. I think this is a little like a "thought experiment"—to use a phrase that was popular in earlier

AND THE MIND OF MAN

20th-century physics, when Einstein, Bohr, and others were thinking out experiments which one did not try to perform but rather tried to use symbolically to figure out concepts and sharpen them. The thought that some day we might be visited from outer space can play a similar role. I do not think that day will ever come, but there is some point in imagining that some day we might be visited. To me, that has all the feeling in it of Judgment Day. Because that would be the point at which mankind would be called to account. How well have we taken care of the solar system and life within it? An interesting question.

QUESTION

Earlier, Professor Wald said that he believed that the Periodic Table had come to an end. I wonder if there is any evidence either way which shows that maybe we have a very incomplete conception of what exists in material form.

WALD

I would like to have a deep argument with somebody on this. My own thoughts came out some time ago, and have not changed recently. To me it is a very important thought that not everything is relative; that a few things are universal. The Periodic System of natural elements runs from 1 to 91, from hydrogen to uranium. Then the transuranic elements by now have run up to 103. That there are other elements beyond 103, I would not doubt. That there are also still undiscovered isotopes, perhaps. But that there is anything more to be found by way of atomic numbers, I am sure is a meaningless question. It is like asking, "Is there some other number on Arcturus between 4 and 5?" The trouble is that some people might think that sounds like a good question. I think it is just a misunderstanding of what a number series means; and the Periodic System of the elements is a simple number series.

QUESTION

I would like to direct a question to Carl Sagan. Professor Wald has raised the issue of the control of technology. Now the conference that took place in Soviet Armenia was a mutual conference between two great powers. Professor Morrison has raised the possibility that a tremendous corpus of knowledge can come wafting down from outer space. Suppose that this comes into an American facility in Puerto Rico, technology that would enable us to dominate this world. Suppose it comes into a Soviet facility in Armenia. What exactly would be the international body that would monitor these signals from outer space, assuming that this civilization that we would be communicating with is more advanced and would be giving us tremendous technological knowledge? What is to guarantee that one of the existing nation-states does not monitor it and use it as we have used our technology in the past?

SAGAN

Very good question. Fortunately, I think it has a quick answer. The answer has to do with time scale and beamwidth. As Phil Morrison stressed, and he *must* be right, the time scale to learn a new technology from such a message must be long—decades, perhaps. No one is going to say, "Put tab A into slot B." You want to think a little before you do that. You do not say, "Oh, yes, sir; right in." You want to understand what is happening first. So things necessarily will move slowly if there is a new technology involved. That is the first part of the answer.

The second part is that the Earth is tiny compared to the size of the beam. Therefore, all of the Earth—not just Armenia and Puerto Rico—but also the Netherlands and Australia and Ghana and all the other countries are going to be able to pick up the same message. Therefore it makes no sense at all for one nation to classify the message. It is like classifying the Sun. It makes no sense. You can do it if you want, but it does not help.

QUESTION

The assumption is that these messages are now passing through the solar system. We have to assume that we are just not receiving them now. If you know that if you are the first country to discover this body of knowledge, you'll have a major advantage, then might not. . . .

SAGAN

Then you have to imagine a scenario in which there is a large, secret radio telescope that is working for a century on a given problem and word never leaks out. I myself find that difficult to believe, especially since the total number of radio astronomers in the world is extremely small, and all of them know each other. Also, I believe that the community of scientists on this issue is such that it is impossible for such a discovery to be made without it being known on an international scale.

WALD

Once again, all the nations will be listening in equally, provided they have equally big radio telescopes. So we will have a radio-telescope race, and God help the nation that has a somewhat smaller radio telescope than the others. As for the community of world science, this is the first time I have heard that it covers weapons technology.

SAGAN

We are not talking about weapons technology.

WALD

But this can be converted into weapons technology.

SAGAN

Sure, but it starts out by saying, "A, B, C, D. . . ." Do you say, "Let's classify the alphabet and maybe the next thing that comes in will be how to build a better weapon"? I just cannot see it.

WALD

But that is the way nuclear energy appeared. One did not know what to do with it or how to handle it, so a few nations with the technical facilities and the wealth got themselves atom bombs.

QUESTION

The assumption has been up to now that any message received will be via some electromagnetic wavelength. It would seem to me that that is a very naive assumption to make in view of the fact that the senders, as has been stated repeatedly, will be far more intelligent than us, and may have access to means of which we are completely unaware.

BERENDZEN

Excellent point. Phil, you have given much thought to this. Would you respond?

AND THE MIND OF MAN

MORRISON

If the thousand-megacycle bands of radio are not the best ones, even though they are easily accessible, then there is no question about it, we will find nothing from this search. The only trouble with that kind of argument is that it could be put forward at any time, no matter what technology is presently available. You can always say there is something we do not know that 10 years from now will be much better understood. Therefore I think if you say this, your inaction is guaranteed; then you surely will never make the search.

And it can be the other way around. When it turns out after sober thought that you find yourself easily able to listen by some means that looks plausible, that will in fact carry the message, then try it. I believe there is a society of these groups, not just one. There are probably very many. If there were only one, we would likely have no hope of finding it. But there are probably thousands, maybe as many as a million. They probably have already had much experience at finding new civilizations and bringing them into the network. If so, they will understand that they should not start with the most advanced device; if you want to make friends with some new group somewhere, you do not set up color TV stations. You might wave a flag or beat a drum. You know you have access to those channels.

SAGAN

I would look at it like this. Suppose that we were a tribe in some isolated valley in, say, New Guinea, where we communicate with our neighbors over in the next valley by runner and by drum. And we are asked to imagine an advanced civilization thousands of miles away. How would they communicate? I would say, "Oh, probably by very fast runners or enormous drums that beat very loud." In fact, there is a vast international radio and cable traffic going around such people, and over them, and through them, and they would not know about it. But that radio and cable traffic is not intended to talk to the inhabitants of that isolated valley. It is intended for conversation between technologically more sophisticated beings. If we wanted to talk to them, then we would need to use the technology of the local civilization.

And I would imagine that if an advanced civilization wanted to talk to us, they would say, "Those guys must be extremely backward. Let's go to some ancient museum and pull out . . . what do you call it? . . . one of those radio telescopes, and beam it at them." But meanwhile they would use for their own purposes whatever it is they use—gravity waves, or neutrinos, or tachyons, or whatever is the fast, high-information channel.

QUESTION

Do you think it is more likely that the message we will intercept will be going back and forth between two members of a society or will it be an exploratory one, aimed just at us?

MORRISON

If we get the message at all, it is not likely to be just a chance beam that crosses us—that is very unlikely.

QUESTION

But it will have a wide beamwidth, as was pointed out.

MORRISON

If it is a wide beam, then the beam would include probably just exactly these search channels
we are talking about. If it is not that, it will be very
hard to find a message that has not been designed to
be easy to read. If it is just high-speed chatter on
some frequency we cannot use, I do not know if we
are ever going to find it.

SAGAN

Wide beam compared to the size of the Earth
but narrow beam compared to how many stars you
are going to pick up.

QUESTION

My question is more philosophical, getting back
to a little while ago, and directs itself primarily to
Professor Stendahl. I would like to think about
what aspect of our idea of God and the ideas of
God around the world—Chinese, for instance, as
well as Judeo-Christian—what aspects of these concepts extrapolate to other beings? What utility
might such extrapolations have?

AND THE MIND OF MAN

STENDAHL

It is very clear that anyone who says "God" is making a universal statement. He is not thinking of God in the narrow sense. There is a long discussion whether high Gods preceded more limited Gods, and so forth. It is so easy for us partly because we often say man created God in his own image; hence there is a Christian God. But a Christian does not claim God to be a Christian God—he claims Him to be God the Creator. And that is where the flaw is—that you mix those up if you see the religious experience from within when you say God, you say God of the universe. Now you can say, "It seems that you claim that, but actually, brother, you really have a tribal concept." Then I have to answer, "I'm sorry, I slipped. I should have known better, and if I speak about God, He is the God of the universe." Frankly, I was serious when I said that the Christian world has lived with angels and archangels and all the company of heaven; there is a lot of experience in thinking about an ever-expanding universe, although in mythological terms rather than terms of telecommunication. I do not know if I meet your question.

QUESTION

I was really wondering what aspects of all of our concepts—what unifying aspects—can be attributed to the concept of other civilizations. One might consider the Taoist idea of God or the tribal God of the Montagnards to be completely alien. I was wondering what discrete aspects of our concept might extrapolate themselves.

STENDAHL

If I understand religion right, it is a very distinct way, a special way, of dealing with reality. *Period.* And if there is additional information about this reality, that is an enriching experience. And that is as simple as that.

BERENDZEN

One final question?

QUESTION

At the beginning Carl Sagan mentioned the number of assumptions involved about extraterrestrial life. And someone mentioned that these as-

98

sumptions lead to millions or billions of civilizations. But I have not heard anyone here put
together a picture of how you believe that there is a
possibility of extraterrestrial life.

BERENDZEN

The reason we have not done that is that it is already in print, and we took it as a "given." Besides
technical papers on it, I might refer you to a couple of popular books, one by Walter Sullivan called
We Are Not Alone, and the other by Shklovskii
and Sagan entitled *Intelligent Life in the Universe.*
The arguments are reviewed in them, and elsewhere.

The basic reasoning, simply put, goes like this.
In our galaxy alone there is a staggeringly large
number of stars—on the order of 10^{11}. During the
last decade or two, we have learned that the probability of stars having planetary systems is high; perhaps as many as one-tenth of the stars have systems
roughly comparable with our own. We must consider only stars with good ecospheres; that is,
spheres in which the conditions are suitable for life
—not too hot, not too cold, just enough UV, etc.

One crucial criterion is temporal stability—that the conditions stay constant long enough for life to begin and evolution to proceed. Even though these criteria are fairly stern and conservative, the number of suitable planets still remains quite high. This type of information comes primarily from astronomy.

Then we join with the biochemists, who tell us about the probable evolution of life here on Earth. For over a decade, evidence has built suggesting that life can arise naturally if the proper substances and conditions are available. The Earth's primordial atmosphere could have produced amino acids, which are basic to DNA molecules, which in turn are basic to life. And recently amino acids have been found in meteorites. And besides that, interstellar molecules, including hydrocarbons, have now been discovered. Thus we know that the ingredients for carbon-based life either already exist in the universe or can be readily manufactured by natural processes; indeed, many of the building blocks of life reside within our own solar system, off of our planet.

If you put these kinds of facts and probabilities together, it leads you to the conclusions we started

AND THE MIND OF MAN

with as initial premises, and with which apparently no one on the panel has disagreed—that is, that other life *must* exist in the universe and that it probably does so in abundance.

Related to that is the sobering thought that if the reasoning on these probabilities is right, then while we have been sitting here talking this afternoon, there are within our galaxy alone—not counting the other billions of galaxies—just within our galaxy there are perhaps a thousand, ten thousand, a million civilizations capable of communicating. Their communications quite possibly are passing through this room and through our very bodies! If we only knew exactly where and how to look. . . .

THE PANELISTS

RICHARD BERENDZEN, astronomy educator and historian of science

Dr. Berendzen is a professor in the Department of Astronomy at Boston University. In 1971 he chaired the International Conference on Education and the History of Modern Astronomy, held under the auspices of the New York Academy of Sciences and the American Astronomical Society. He was a member of the Astronomy Survey Committee of the National Academy of Sciences and of the Education Commission of the International Astronomical Union. His course at Boston University entitled "Search for Life in the Universe," was one of the first on this topic in the United States. He is a fellow of the American Association for the Advancement of Science and an editor of the *Journal of College Science Teaching*.

ASHLEY MONTAGU, anthropologist, social biologist, and author

Dr. Montagu was formerly chairman of the Department of Anthropology at Rutgers University. He is best known as the author of more than 40 books in the social sciences. In 1969 he published *Man, His First Two Millions Years*, which touches on the theme of the symposium. Among his best known books are *Man's Most Dangerous Myth: The Fallacy of Race; Introduction to Physical Anthropology; Human Heredity;* and *The Natural Superiority of Women.* He is a fellow of the American Association for the Advancement of Science and an editor of the National Historical Society Series.

PHILIP MORRISON, physicist, educator, and philosopher of science

Dr. Morrison is a professor in the Physics Department at the Massachusetts Institute of Technology. His interests have ranged over many areas of science, and he has written on the impact of science and technology on society. In 1955 he received the Pregel Prize, in 1957 the Babran Prize, and in 1965 the Oerstad Medal, awards based on his contributions to physics and education. He is a fellow of the American Association for the Advancement of Science and a member of the National Academy of Sciences. He regularly reviews books in *Scientific American* on almost all fields related to science. In his early career, Professor Morrison's research was primarily in nuclear physics, but during the past 15 years it has shifted increasingly into astrophysics. Also, for many years he has worked on reform in science education at all levels.

AND THE MIND OF MAN

CARL SAGAN, astronomer and exobiologist

Dr. Sagan is director of the Laboratory for Planetary Studies at Cornell University. He is the author of several books on planetary science, and he coauthored with I. S. Shklovskii *Intelligent Life in the Universe*, published in 1966. Dr. Sagan is a pioneer in the field of exobiology—the study of evidence for extraterrestrial life. He has been a member of various advisory groups for NASA and the National Academy of Sciences. In 1971, he was the chairman of the U.S. Organizing Committee for the Joint Conference of the U.S. National and Soviet Academies of Sciences on Communication with Extraterrestrial Intelligence. He is a fellow of the American Association for the Advancement of Science, and an editor of *Icarus* and of several other publications.

KRISTER STENDAHL, clergyman and theologian

Dr. Stendahl has been Dean of the Harvard School of Theology since 1968. Born in Stockholm, he was a priest in the Church of Sweden and a professor at Uppsala University before coming to Harvard in 1954. He is a fellow of the American Academy of Arts and Sciences and a member of the Nathan Soederblom Society. Also, he is on the Executive Council of the Lutheran Church of America, is an editor of the *Harvard Theological Review*, and is on the executive committee of the American Association of Theology Schools. His several books include *The School of St.*

105

LIFE BEYOND EARTH

Matthew and Its Use of the Old Testament; The Bible and the Role of Women; and *The Scrolls and the New Testament*, which he edited and coauthored.

GEORGE WALD, biologist

Dr. Wald is a professor in the Biological Laboratories at Harvard University. In 1967 he won the Nobel Prize in medicine for his work in physiology. His other prizes include the Lilly award of the American Chemical Society, the Ives medal of the Optical Society of America, the Proctor medal of the Association for Research in Opthalmology, the Lasker Award of the American Public Health Association, and the Rumford Medal of the American Academy of Arts and Sciences. Besides his pioneering work on the chemistry and physiology of vision, his research has included studies of biochemical evolution. He is a fellow of the American Association for the Advancement of Science and a member of the National Academy of Sciences and the American Philosophical Society.

106

☆ U. S. GOVERNMENT PRINTING OFFICE : 1973 O - 502-823